SHE...

by

Olesya Sytnik

DORRANCE
PUBLISHING CO
EST. 1920
PITTSBURGH, PENNSYLVANIA 15238

Dorrance Publishing Co
585 Alpha Drive
Suite 103
Pittsburgh, PA 15238
Visit our website at *www.dorrancebookstore.com*

ISBN: 978-1-6386-7247-0
eISBN: 978-1-6386-7599-0

THIS BOOK IS FOR YOU

Hmmm… why did I decide to write this book? Well, plain and simple it started with me catching myself on believing in magic. Magic of the first kiss, magic of love from first sight, magic of a laughing child, magic of believing in something you know yourself doesn't exist. I live for those moments when everything stops, nothing exists, and you connect with yourself. I love seeing kids laugh. Just the sound of the innocent, genuine, and pure laugh. Nothing else matters, kids don't have agendas, they don't think about bills and dinner plans. At that moment, when kids laugh, nothing else matters. They express the most innocent and simple emotion—happiness. At that moment, all they are is happy. Their eyes are full of life, their minds are free, they are just simply happy.

And then I started questioning if that is possible for all of us to follow that same framework, to be pure, to be genuine, to be free. And, understandably, not all day, every day, but just once in a while. Can you imagine how much lighter we'd be, how much better we'd feel if we just occasionally believed in magic, believed in something ridiculous and send our minds on a journey to absolutely nowhere in particular. Just away….

We are superheroes, each and every one of us, we all have … powers. We are all exposed to the magic of brilliantly understanding or confusing the hell out one another. We experience passion, love, jealousy, anger, vulnerability, frustration, constant dialogue within ourselves, and so much more. Every emotion we encounter has power over us, enabling us to cry, laugh, think, distance, or pull close. To me, it is important to become aware of those powers, explore them and appreciate them for what they are, appreciate what I have, what I was gifted or blessed with. Every mile, every turn, every detour has a huge impact on the destination ahead of us. Just know, that every finish line is the beginning of a new race. Go the distance, reach for answers, question everything you feel.

Connecting with yourself, being alone and feeling content in this universe is actually what connects us together, what holds us together, what makes us realize that, in fact, we aren't alone; we have one another. And that is the real power. Becoming aware of who we are is the power, and we all possess it. We are only afraid to tap into it; we are terrified of looking into ourselves and learning about every little detail we consist of, every spark, every marble, every thought.

We are prisoners of our own ... We are courageous, brilliant, right and wrong, genius and incredibly silly, hopeful, destroyed, happy, and vulnerable piles of mess. And I say mess as a compliment. We cannot choose to be one way or another. We are everything at once! Like I said, mess.

My hopes are that this book will bring joy to readers, make them think, question, detach, get close, laugh, and cry. Whatever emotion wakes up while you read this book, please hold on to it, keep it in your heart, and never let go. Be you! By being alone and searching within ourselves we actually become stronger, we get attracted to the energy that comes from within, and that truly is power.

So, pour yourself a glass of wine or water. Have a sip of strong espresso or a cup of tea. Get comfy on the couch or outside on the deck. In reality, none of it matters. Just take a few minutes to read. Set aside the day-to-day routine and make some time for yourself, breathe ... and ... be magical. ★

CHAPTER ONE
She is searching...

We are all searching for something, wondering what is happening to us, to life, to our belongings, to our feelings, to our kids and so on. She is also searching. She is searching for answers, answers to simple questions. Simple questions that come together and become a story. Best stories are told quietly, behind closed doors, with a glass of Shiraz in hand, looking into the flames of fire. Peaceful, dangerous and deep... fire? Maybe... but also questions, questions that may be so hard to put together, process, and ask. How do you compose the question? How do you get to convey the exact meaning you are searching for? In what language? In what tense? How? And then she stops...

Takes a deep breath...

With a sip of an excellent red wine, closes her eyes, wipes the tear from her cheek and tells her story. No words, quietly, barely moving, mostly just breathing. The story of searching for answers, simple answers. What is she? She is lost, she is convinced she needs to get lost to find herself, to find that connection within herself again. She takes her broken wings and tries to fly again. Why search? Why put herself through a painful and time-consuming search? Is it really worth it? Stories... stories untold, stories made up, stories unfinished. Wine, a delicate touch, a smooth way of unveiling stories she wasn't gonna tell. She speaks, she screams ... quietly. With one look, with one breath, with one touch. Shhhhhhh...

Another sip...

Another glass...

Another bottle...

Another day...

...the search continues; she is determined, she is motivated, and inspired. She wants to know; she wants to feel, feel more, feel stronger, feel... just feel... She wants to feel, she desires to find herself, she aches for answers, she reaches for the truth. She needs to know.... She takes another sip, wipes another tear and tells stories... ★

1

CHAPTER TWO
She is incredible...

Have you ever heard the glass shatter? Have you ever felt the cuts? Deep ... Sharp ... Painful ... This is when you realize that you are falling—falling fast, you are just like that glass, you shatter, you break, you fall apart into million pieces. The break, heart break, bones break inside, your breath stops ... Everything stops and it is incredible ... Now you are a pile, pile of shattered glass, broken feelings, crushed bones, smeared dreams. You stop living and you start existing. Your daily existence is nothing more than just a hope to get through the day and start over again tomorrow.

She was broken, she felt nothing, she was numb, hurt, discouraged, and disabled in a way. Nothing mattered to her. She lost the ability to love and feel loved. It is scary when you stop feeling, when you don't care. It gets dark and she was in the dark. Heartbeat, pulse gone ... Scary ...

Heartbeat, pulse ... scary ... scary when the light comes in for the first time. When you start coming out of the darkness and you really don't know what to expect. It is scary to start feeling again ... scary but also incredible ... So incredible ... Not the darkness but the light ... She is my light ... She gives me hope, love, happiness. She makes the pain go away. She doesn't realize how much she means to her. All of a sudden, life has a meaning ... again ... It's incredible. It feels incredible ... She is incredible ... And again, she is falling—falling fast ... falling in love, falling in love with life. Wow. Her life is a puzzle, she completes it, she keeps her sane, she holds her together, she is her anchor, she is her light.

HERS ... Wow. Hers ... So many *her* comes to mind. Her love, her hope, her happiness, her everything, her dreams ... her child, her daughter. This is crazy, unbelievable, and completely unrealistic to have this much power in her tiny hands.

3

OLESYA SYTNIK

She misses her every day, every hour, every minute, every second ....
Every time she closes my eyes, she sees her, she feels her... she feels, she
feels again and it is incredible ... She is incredible ... And life goes on,
thanks to her little angel. ★

CHAPTER THREE
She is trying…

Fire and water … Beautiful, powerful, peaceful, damaging, and destroying at times. Two simple things that can be so different, that can be so much more than just something to look at.

Water… Peaceful, calm and beautiful until you go under, until you can't breathe, until it takes over you. Every breath, every second. Quiet killer. Still so beautiful and so powerful.

Fire… Wow, amazing, strong, beautiful, breathtaking, powerful, and so damaging. It burns you alive, it swallows you into a fascinating world where anything can be destroyed.

She feels it; she feels both at the same time. How is it possible? She can't breathe, she can't think, everything stops. Her heart stops. Her feelings, her dreams and hopes towards the future together burn… She watches it burn within herself, she feels it burn … Beautiful fire, destroying power. It gets better over time; she gets used to the heat. It's now warm, calm, and nice to look at. Burned hopes, burned feelings, burned happiness and destroyed love. Piece by piece, little by little all becomes ashes. Quiet killer, killing everything— killing the world. Her world, he was her world. He gave her the world and burned it at once.

She wants me to drink, water gives life, and water keeps you going until it takes you under. She can't breathe. Water also kills. She is drowning; there is no air, no chance to get out. She burns and she drowns at the same time. He destroyed her, destroyed them, the world they were creating.

She wants to live; she wants to enjoy looking at the water and fire from afar. She doesn't want it killing her, like it is now. They both are beautiful and powerful, and she doesn't want them destroying her anymore. She'll stay afloat; she'll put out the fire. She'll be fine. They'll be fine. She doesn't want to burn or drown anymore. She can't, she is broken and numb. She wants to start feeling again, she wants to not hurt anymore, and she wants to live. He was the water to her fire until it pulled her under. She is letting go and trying to swim again. ★

CHAPTER FOUR
She is tired...

... finally, off work, many thoughts go through her mind. She makes the call. What is clear? On the other end of the phone line—constant jealousy, show off, asking for attention. Attention. How important is it? We all ask for it, but do we ever think of the ways we are using toward something so insignificant? She doesn't see the value in the conversation; she sees through it; she knows how insignificant it really is. She knows... in a girl world, there is no friendship, there is no compassion, there is no pure.

Wait... pure. Let's take it back, there is pure. Pure manipulation, pure jealousy, pure hunger. Hunger is another interesting concept. Hunger always drives us. Drives the good, the bad, the incredibly senseless and sometimes immoral acts. Acts of kindness, acts of despair, acts of whatever it is that we are driven to. She is strong... but she is tired.

She doesn't want to be strong; she wants to be tired once in a while, she wants to be cared for, she wants... peace. Here it is, she is, once again, tired... . Long day at the office, ridiculously hot drive home and ... finally, she was there, where she belonged, with the little munchkin. The munchkin who is always by her side, even when they're apart. Here it is, pure love, pure feeling of complete, genuine love, connection and huge relief. She is happy. Tired but happy. That's the crazy part. You don't need anything tangible to feel complete. You need you, you need open, you need love, you need time, time alone with people who matter. She makes time, something so simple, ordinary and yet, so grand. Time... she invests *time* into happiness, even though lost at times, tired at times, sad at times.

And that is exactly it, you can sit there and complain about so many things in life, but tired *will* consume you, swallow you whole. She understands, once you let darkness in, it never comes out. So, she puts it aside, tired is a side note. Tired is no more, only happiness, only positive and only forward. Kind is strong, positive is strong, genuine is strong. Tired, jealous, unhappy, whatever other excuse you come up with and try to cover up with *tired* is weak, is wrong and is not her cup-a-tea. ★

CHAPTER FIVE

She is numb...

It is fascinating to see the way we all deal with the same situations so differently. Same hurt, same love, same happiness, same cold, same jealousy, same frustration and same ... hurt? She knows... she feels... she understands... the hurt—the only constant in every single person's life that remains unchanged, unmasked, and completely unpredictable. It is ... a mystery, she is a mystery. Hurt...

Mystery...

She is not a mystery, she is crazy! What is so mysterious about hurt? The cause of pain, the feeling that can trigger a handful of emotions at once or nothing at all. It is power ... she is power ... she is strong, but she is tired. Tired of hurt, tired of pain, tired of craving the burn but fearing the ice.

Fear... keeps her focused on the past, the repeat of that past, making the same mistakes from ... the ... past. She is weak ... she is powerless ... and she is tired. Same concept, another angle. Forget it, get away, stop!

Ice... Not sure what is better, feeling it all or being cold. Maybe both, feeling ... the cold. She is cold. Cold... not for the lack of heat, warm clothes and blankets, but for the lack of feeling. That moment she realizes that she does not even know what it is she's feeling. Cold ... nothing burns more than that. Seems so crazy and fascinating, beautiful insanity, cold and burn— both at once.

What is worse? Feel the burn or not feel at all? We cause pain ... to ourselves, to others, she knows pain, she speaks pain, she's tired and very cold, lacking the "feeling" gene, cold ... not temperature wise but numb. Numb feels good, numb feels safe, safe of feeling and burning.

9

OLESYA SYTNIK

Safe...
No more sad...
No more tired...
No more pain...
... She wants to feel but shelters herself from feeling too much. Just like she absolutely loves the rain but shelters herself from it with an umbrella.... ★

CHAPTER SIX
She is aching...

Small things, simple things, ridiculous and insignificant things ... Appreciate it, be silly, be childish, be unpredictable. Learn from kids, be kids ... Love, open up, accept and trust, be free ... She looks around. The hectic routine, busy life style, countless bills, stress and chaos. It has become the new norm.

Emptiness...

Heartbeat...

Scream...

She wants to run away, away from this new norm, away from negative, away from pressure, back into simple. Here is that word again—simple. Simple is by definition "uncomplicated." She wants uncomplicated, like it was once before. Genuine uncomplicated life. We complicate things, we make it all complicated, we mess it all up. We mess up the nice and easy existence and make it into a swirl of stuff, complicated stuff, unnecessary and hard to deal with stuff ...

Ridiculous...

Running away ... Running away without moving. We all run away differently, we take different types of transportation and different routes. Close your eyes, meditate and fly away from reality, fly high and go deep ... look deep inside, so deep that you can see inside your veins. Connect, connect with yourself, be yourself ... for once ... just be. Take a sip of wine, or take a shot, or maybe three, run away, escape the emptiness and chaos. Release the demons and let them have a drink with you. Just this once, create a carefree environment,

11

disconnect, detach, find … you … Remember you? Pray … pray until it hurts, pray until you can't control your tears. Take your guardian angels' hands and allow them to hold you, fill yourself up with good, connect within, find … you … Remember you!

She cries, she laughs, she screams, she prays, and she drinks. She is trying to uncomplicate the complicated existence and it's beautiful. Beautiful chaos, ridiculously impossible happiness, aching for peace and joy. She is being herself, and that's worth every mess up, every drink and every prayer, every laugh and every tear. ★

CHAPTER SEVEN
She is love...

Power ... Power of love. Love ... L. O. V. E. Will it conquer all or is it just the four-letter word that will stab us in the back? She questions love, the reasons we love and actions that support that non-sense concept of loving someone till death do you part, of giving each other all we got to show the pure feeling and emotion of compassion, the concept so simple and complicated at the same time that confuses the heck out of parties involved, concept that can make you feel complete or entirely empty, something that can build you and break you to pieces, award you with confidence or paranoia. What is love? What is the right way to love? Do we even love? Do we know how to?

The Holy Bible tells us that "Love is patient, love is kind. It does not envy, it does not boast, it is not proud. It is not rude, it is not self-seeking, it is not easily angered, it keeps no record of wrongs. Love does not delight in evil but rejoices with the truth. It always protects, always trusts, always hopes, always perseveres, never fails."

Love...

Patience...

Envy...

Pride...

Anger...

Hope...

She's confused and completely disoriented by the perception of love, something so pure and ridiculously complicated. If love is patient, then why do we rush into finding it so desperately? If love is kind, then why do we hate each other and treat each other poorly for not meeting the societal standards (or our own standards for that matter)? If love does not envy, then why is there so much jealousy towards people receiving it? If love is not proud, then why do people gloat in its existence? If it's not rude, then why do we get disturbed and bothered by it so easily? If it is not angry, then why were there so many people killed in the name of love? If love isn't wrong, then why do we tell each other how to love us the right way? If it's not evil, then why do we plot revenge against people we once loved? If love is based on truth, then why do we lie to get someone to love us in return? If love protects, then why were there wars declared to show that love for God, religious beliefs, loyalty, for people, for cultures, families and countries? If love perseveres, then why do we hear "I don't love you anymore" from people, who once were the foundation of love? If love never fails, then why are there so many failed marriages and abandoned kids?

Where is love? What is love? Is there love?

She believes in love, or believed it rather, once upon too many times. Here it is: Love is blind! Love is a mask, Love is power. Love is two-faced, Love is danger. Heard the saying "Dangerously in love?" Exactly! Love is an obelisk and an easily folded house of cards. It is a light summer breeze and an ice storm. It brings you to tears and sets your heart on fire, it gives you hope and shatters you into million sparks.

Love … She is genuine and she is love … She believes in love. She gives, she waits, she hopes and protects.

There is love. She is Love. But what is love? All she knows, that "… love is like the wind, you can't see it, but you can feel it…" As far as understanding it … give up already, love makes no sense, love has no name, love has no fear and love has no reason. She is convinced, the verdict is in! Love is … a beautifully conceptualized and an unreasonably dangerous mess…

She is a mess… ★

CHAPTER EIGHT
She makes mistakes...

Mistakes were made, but not by me ... That is the delusional perception of each and every person on this beautiful planet. We are always quick to judge but not too quick to acknowledge our own shortcomings. Regardless of right or wrong, we must be able to have a dialogue within. A dialogue with yourself, within yourself, by yourself. An open, honest and genuine dialogue that helps you to realize things you don't talk about, things you don't disclose to anyone, things masked and hidden under a million layers of significant only to you reasons to not open up, to not be seen, to not be vulnerable.

Vulnerability ... is power. Vulnerability makes her weak. She is not weak, she is strong, she is invincible, and she needs no one! Invincible ... She won't be defeated by fears of the shallow society that knows nothing about her, she needs no one, she wants nothing, she is fine. Brilliant! She is brilliant, absolutely brilliant, and she is invincible. Wait ... invincible or invisible? At some point one becomes the other. There is a border between the two powerful states of mind. There is a bridge to walk back and forth. Not walk but run rather. Run from one state of mind to the next, run because

it is easier than dealing with pain and responsibility. Don't be stuck! You are invincible … you are invisible.

Brilliant confusion. Mistakes are made…

She makes mistakes. Invisible to the world but significant to her. With all the advancements in communication technology, there is still nothing more effective than the sound of a human voice, your voice. Talk, hear, listen to yourself, within yourself. Just breathe and realize, that dialogue is important. Connect all the lose parts of yourself by talking, talking to yourself, talking in yourself.

Here it is … Power of communication. On some level it is the greatest power we possess. She talks … and talks … and talks some more … She talks … dialogue … power. She makes mistakes, and they are no longer invisible. Break away, be weak, be vulnerable, be that dialogue. That is when we are the strongest, when we become aware of our weaknesses, when we break away from the brilliant concept of "no one cares" and start opening up.

She is strong.

She is vulnerable.

She is brilliant.

Mistakes are made …

… by her. ★

CHAPTER NINE
She is incomplete…

When two points are destined to touch, the universe will always find a way to connect them, even if the direct connection is not possible. We choose our ways; we always make a choice that will lead us to something new and exciting. Well maybe not always exciting as we may take the wrong turn, make the wrong choice and burn, burn on the incorrectly chosen path. In truth, all the choices we make always start with love…

Love…

Power…

We are never complete, we always move towards something, search for something, look for something or someone. We are never fully complete. We are always trying to complete a certain puzzle of our lives: finish a book, make dinner, write a grocery list, take a shower, mow the lawn … find love. Constant incomplete puzzles of life.

… Puzzle—no need to make sense of it, just accept it…. We are never complete. She loves puzzles … piece by piece creating an incredible picture. It can be anything, she can be anything. In the moment of looking for the right pieces of the puzzles, she feels accomplished, satisfied, happy even. Puzzles are incredible. We believe that at some point in the future we will figure out every piece and where it goes, every corner, every little piece…

Pieces…

Her life is a puzzle and she builds it, day by day, piece by piece, hoping to complete it, but is it ever complete? We make our lives out of hopes and chaos. She hopes … She hopes to complete the puzzle.

Another hour…

Another day…

Missing pieces. There are still pieces missing, always looking for bigger, better, more … More of everything, needing more pieces, more laughter, more love, more warmth, more happiness, more … to feel complete, to complete a picture and start on another. It never stops, she never stops … puzzles keep coming, pieces go missing, pieces got put in the wrong places, but she has faith. That foolish belief in something that is not logically rational, but still … power … faith in completing a perfect picture, connecting those two pieces in the universe that are destined to be together, to make a whole.

And life goes on, she is puzzled but also … hopeful … that one day she is

… complete. ★

CHAPTER TEN
She is two-faced...

Deception ... Friend or foe? Act of destroying or healing? As humans, we are always on crossroads, we are always thinking, contemplating, choosing and evaluating ... everything. We love. We love but hurt one another in the process. We hurt ourselves. We manipulate the truth we're after. We tell each other lies; we tell ourselves lies. For what?

... Listen ... Ready? To avoid the hurt! Bizarre concept ... We are so immersed into this ridiculous idealistic ritual of lying, that we convinced ourselves that it is, in fact, okay to do if ... we do it in the name of love, care, and compassion. When did we stop believing in pure love, honesty and genuine feelings?

Lie...

for

Love...

What a powerful concept!

Is it true that our day-to-day strategy of existence is nothing more than a game theory-based environment? Two-faced ... is this the new us? Is she two-faced? Is she everyone's best friend until the moment she's not? Is that a new way of living or is it just a safe approach to this world's negativity and anger? Here it is, anger ... another powerful emotion we are not totally sure how to handle. Did we all become cold? Did we lose faith in love? Do we only rationalize our action by focusing on winning, no matter the cost?

Love hurts ...

Manipulation ...

Deception ...

Do we only exist in each other's lives to get manipulated to our advantage when the right time comes? She looks for more than being a contingency, not interested in becoming a victim of circumstances. She is not manipulative or deceiving, she is smart at dealing with other people, seeing through them and understanding the possibilities and behaviors. She doesn't guess, she only merely tries to read people, like books, books full of surprises and unpredictable twists. She is two-faced, and it's not a bad thing!

Everything is split in half: left and right, two-way streets, two-sided coins, heads and tails, and there is nothing wrong with it! She is happy and sad, energetic and tired, loving and numb, fire and ice.

   She makes choices for the greater good, she brings people into her life for selfish reasons, to love, to care, to learn from and to hold. Hold close to heart, hold close to soul … no game … no theory … only selfish reasons of benefiting from their love and healing energy.

   Love heals …
       She heals …
           herself with love. ★

CHAPTER ELEVEN
She jumps…

Have you ever wanted something so bad that you felt like you'd do almost anything to get it? Or better yet, have you ever experienced the inability to put into words what is it you want, but you want it so badly, it hurts. And you are anxious, excited and want to scream it from the top of the mountain but cannot come up with words. Having no idea how to describe what it is, but still dying to share with the world. Talk, scream, cry, break through … share … communicate, find a way to get through, break through, break …

Break old habits, get away from the routine, move into new jobs, take risk, jump … We are prisoners of our own fears, we are paralyzed and scared to take a step into the unknown. She is a prisoner. Not of fear, not of disbelief, but of inability to share.

Risk …

Taking risk is terrifying but also can be so rewarding. How does that saying go? Translated from Russian it says exactly this: "If you don't risk, you are not worthy of a champagne…." No pain, no gain … Big chances are never small stakes … Same concept.

Why risk? Why take chances and change things? Why shake it up? What if she fails, what if she makes the wrong turn, what if there is a dead end, what if everything disappears into thin air … heartbeat … breathing …

Is it wrong to go into the unknown, walking blindfolded into a world of possibilities? And maybe, just maybe she doesn't fail. And maybe, just maybe there is light … light of bigger and better. And maybe the roads were under construction this whole time for a reason, maybe endless detours and broken bridges finally come together in some weird and ridiculously impossible way. Maybe the dead end is really a pot of gold at the end of the rainbow, that same rainbow that always seemed so far away.

21

OLESYA SYTNIK

What if all those things she's been terrified of are now only a mirage and a shadow of previous disasters?

She talks without finding the right words …

She screams without any sound …

She cries without tears rolling down her cheeks …

It's not always a bad thing—to be unable…. She breaks through. Here it is: no pain, no hurt, no doubts. Only risk, only truth, only champagne.

Shhhhh…

She takes a deep breath, closes her eyes,

lets go of uncertainties and worries, and … jumps. ★

CHAPTER TWELVE
She is a perfect storm…

Have you ever watched the weather forecast? Fascinating process of conceptualizing our future based on predictions of a weatherman. Storms don't just happen, they build their strength overtime, over days, weeks and months even, while terrifying the world of the possible danger coming. We cannot see the future, but we always try to, we try to plan for it, we take preventative measures, we wait…

Waiting …

Another powerful concept. We are terrified of the unknown but is it truly the worst?

What about the aspect of the future when you know what's going to happen, wouldn't that be the real terror, most frightening and breathtaking experience? Expecting and waiting for the inevitable to come. There is nothing more terrifying than the future, but we are still anxious to see what it brings. She recognizes herself in a storm, unpredictable, destroying.

Power…

Connection…

You can't connect with a storm, you can't touch it, hug it or even get close. The storm hugs you, it draws you in, it swallows you whole. We imagine the perfect connection, we paint it so flawlessly in our hearts, and then it starts … the search for that flawless connection begins. We come up with that image in the dark, while watching the quiet sky, beautiful stars, peaceful night. And then we begin the search, in the chaos of the daylight, routine and traffic. Traffic of thoughts, hopes, desires and overwhelming ideas. Perfectly imperfect future is built on searching for that peace, peace that you find in a storm, in its terrifying and destroying power.

OLESYA SYTNIK

She wants to find peace, peace in the chaos, happiness within terror and satisfaction within the storm.

She is unpredictable …

She is chaos …

She is a perfect storm …

… searching for a peace within herself. ★

CHAPTER THIRTEEN
She doesn't think twice...

Living in the world of endless possibilities, we are still unable to make our lives bright, memorable, mesmerizing, fantastic. We look at the stars in hopes to find answers, we pray in hopes to find guidance, we admire other people's life styles in hopes to find our own ways. We shelter ourselves from that amazing connection to the world, connection we can find within us and extend further. We whisper our wishes to each other, completely convinced that the quieter we say it, the more chances it'll come true. Do we really have to hush our wishes for them to come true...?

She is the writer of her own destiny, she is not cold but rather content, she is set in her own ways and hopes to find that someone, someone who will change her mind about ... everything. We live in the world of constraints, and the main constraint is time. Stop... Time does not exist, concept of now is not real, but timelessness is.

She makes up her own rules, she creates a world of nonsense. World where nothing is what it is, and everything is what it isn't. Different? I'd say so. World where time has no significance and all moments are equally real, world that allows her to truly feel and connect to every cell of her mind, world where no one can hurt her, and she is in total control.

There are infinite ways to communicate.

Whisper ...

Whisper into the silence.

Listen ...

Listen to the symphony of stars.

Write ...

Write secret messages and send them in a bottle into the ocean.

Have fun now, don't stop living. Don't wait for a perfect ending, because it always is only the beginning. Nothing ever ends, and every ending is really the beginning of the next best thing. Don't think, don't analyze, don't freeze, don't shelter yourself from the possibilities of this amazing and unique world. You are a part of it,

    ... she is a part of it.

    She is a part of this nonsense unique world with endless possibilities, she whispers to the stars, she connects her hopes with mind, she lives her life, she doesn't stop.

    And just like that ... time dissolves into the ocean she calls "destiny."

    No doubts ...

    She lives, she hopes, she loves ... she doesn't spin ... she rips off the band aid ...

    ... and she doesn't think twice. ★

CHAPTER FOURTEEN
She is broken…

In the deepest and darkest nights, we realize things we've never thought of, we discover truths about ourselves and we make choices. Hard to believe, but in those moments, we are most vulnerable to ourselves, our dreams and our desires. We crave to be understood, we crave to understand ourselves, understand others.

We are all just a little broken, some more than others but that's what makes us unique, beautiful even.

Broken bones, broken dolls, broken dreams, broken dishes, broken hearts… At different stages of our lives, we experience different brokenness. Funny… She looks back and realizes that each time she was broken, she got up and became stronger. She's built of broken pieces. The more she breaks, the stronger she becomes. Extraordinary discovery, again, in the middle of the night, in deep sleep, in the dark. Crazy but true, how much more comes to lights in the dark. Darkness reveals light, opens her eyes and allows her to see, to discover, to understand. Understand simple things that were kept in the dark, kept pushed away, kept far down her throat.

And now it's hard to breathe. As she is gasping for air, she understands pain, she's reaching for water, she counts her scars. Scars that may not be visible, scars that don't always heal. Within moments … she realizes that maybe, … just maybe she is not broken, just bent, bent over a failed dream or someone else's fairytale. Feeling … interrupted from the ideally structured plan, overdosed on missed opportunities, discouraged from moving forward … she is hugged by darkness.

And only then, inside this beautiful nightmare, she can see the light. We are all designed to look for positive, to give the benefit of the doubt, to stand up straight and come back from ruins of broken dreams into the reality, that maybe … even better than planned before.

OLESYA SYTNIK

Breathe …
Dark …
Peace …
… Good morning. Another cup of coffee, another dream, another broken piece put together. And all goes as planned, the sun is out, the light is in. Breathe …

Sometimes even the most beautiful people are beautifully broken. ★

CHAPTER FIFTEEN
She is still the same...

Change … Close your eyes and think for a moment, think of a moment, a moment that inspires you to be better. What is change? Do we ever change? Are we capable of changing … ourselves, each other, habits, feelings, life… ? Believing in change drives us to make steps into the future, take risks, move places, buy art, get married, color our hair, use bright red lipstick … There are so many things we can change, improve, or run away from.

Change is an amazing, incredibly insane world of a complete fog. You can't see in the fog. Everything that comes out of the fog is unexpected. Take a minute and relax. Close your eyes, detach from the routine and planning for just that minute. Fall … Fall into nothing, detach from time and chaos, just breathe. Shhh… Think of change, think of what you want to change, think of what you are capable to change. And let's be honest, as human beings, our intelligence allows us to change … well … really anything. We just need to be willing to accept that change, risk for it, love it and step into the future.

Take a step …

OLESYA SYTNIK

She is confident, the greatest tragedy is to lose, to be convinced that change is not an option. The inability to change paralyzes us, disables the motivation to be better, and blocks the paths for growth. Here is another revolutionary reminder: "The more things change, the more they stay the same." What? Serious? Where is logic in that? We change only to stay the same? Or do we subconsciously know the path we are taking and strictly following the invisible clues to get there?

Fall …

Risk …

Change it up a little! … She adds some creamer to her coffee, enjoys the new flavor, smell and experience! Afterall, it is still that same amazing cup of black coffee she is so used to. Simple hot beverage that warms her up and makes her look at the world from a different perspective. You can't breathe the air that's been frozen. So warm up, open up, welcome the change, welcome the warmth, be better. Detach from "same," from chaos, be that change, be different, be intelligent, be … anything, simply anything. Go! Invest in an incredible piece of art, have a glass of ridiculously expensive but oh so smooth glass of champagne, be your unique "self." Buy a different floor lamp. As ludicrous as it sounds, do it! Believe me, the light will still be the same, but the way you see it will make all the difference.

Run …

She runs away from the all the same and boring stuff she is so attached to. She runs through fog, she's seeking change. Finally, …

Another town …

Changed look …

Wearing bright red lipstick …

Sipping on a hazelnut flavored coffee …

She stops, she takes a deep breath, she looks up, and she smiles. Same sky, same stars, same her.

… The more things change, the more they stay the same. ★

CHAPTER SIXTEEN
She is the reason...

Everything happens for a reason. Surprise, everyone has heard it about a million times, and thought it to themselves another million times over. Everything doesn't just happen, but it happens ... for a reason. You are the reason. Be the reason! Become the reason.

She is the reason; she is her own path to success. No maps, no manuals, no directions ... just a dream, a dream to be better, a goal to go further, a try to jump higher. We are the success, we are the dream, we are the will power. We are the reasons our dreams come true.

She is true ...

She is true to herself, to her dreams and to her deepest desires. She treasures everything, every day, every ounce of happiness. Even the longest and toughest days become amazing adventures when filled with laughter, positivity and magic of love. Love *you*.

Remember *you*? Don't think of the time, don't count the years, don't watch the minutes to aimlessly pass by. Be simple, be humble, be genuine.

Remember the magic of "simple." We tend to always look for happiness, and forget that it is all around us, it is within us, and it is powerful. Simple is powerful. You don't think so? Try to be silly, in a good way, fun way, simple way. Put on your winter jacket in the middle of a beautiful summer day. Chances are—you'll get swept away with a certain memory from the last time you wore that jacket. Check the pockets. Chances are—you'll find that lucky penny or two. Regardless of heads or tails, love that moment, hold on to that moment ... two seconds, two minutes, two hours ... Time makes no difference. Just hold on, hold on to love, hold on to happiness, love your happiness.

She is a secret ... secret to her own happiness.

In this town ...

OLESYA SYTNIK

In this dimension …

In this mysterious world …

In the world of possibilities, be that possibility, be that drive, be the force, be you. Remember *you*. Be the map, be the direction, be the light.

Everything does happen for a reason, and that reason is … you. ★

CHAPTER SEVENTEEN
She is selfish...

Real interests of people became (for lack of a better word) banal, don't you think? We are very specific in what's important to us: to eat tasty food, have a drink, watch a good show (preferably funny or sad, well, anything that would make us feel at least something), dream of something grand and barely possible. We are amazing. As we dream of all this, we'd like to lounge on our comfy couches, covered by fluffy blankets, and just wait ... wait for it all to just happen to us, preferably all at once.

We all want money, shorter work days, long vacations and exotic travels, fun parties and good sex. Let's be honest, all these are significant factors in our lives, and we are entitled to it all. The most important thing about all these experiences we are fantasizing about, we feel the need to photograph and post everything for the whole world to see. It's almost like we don't live for ourselves. We do not strive to satisfy our own selfish desires, but focus on everyone else's, making everyone aware of what it is we are doing.

Stop ...

Reevaluate ...

When was the last time you met someone who got under your skin? When was the last time you genuinely got attached to someone who turned your world upside down, literally? Have you ever met someone and suddenly became unable to speak, unable to think, unable to breathe? Have you ever missed someone well before you ever told them goodbye? Have you ever planned to see that person again way before the current date is over? Has anyone ever made you feel intoxicated, in the best way possible, without any alcohol, with just a scent of their hair, their smile, their touch, making you slur the words and feel completely detached from this planet?

That's the real desire ... real selfish "I want it now, and not a second later" feeling. Be selfish, be passionate, desire the burn! That's the power, find that power, be that power.

Seek ...

Burn ...

Ache ...

She seeks, she burns, she aches in her desires, they swallow her whole. She is "one of many" and "many in one." She will remind you of everyone at once. Everyone ... you were affectionate towards, people you hated, people you loved and people you wish you'd never known. She is your memory trigger and amnesia, angel and devil, a blessing and a curse. She is a complex formula of incredibly complicated parts, parts of the whole, parts that are constantly missing and found, lost and reorganized, complete and broken.

Look ...

Search ...

Stay ...

Find that one, who will make your body tremble from a simple thought of an insignificant but oh so burning touch, of the non-physical contact with physical reaction, throughout your body, in your heart, through your soul.

Be selfish ...

Burn ... ★

CHAPTER EIGHTEEN
She is losing it...

We are all a little conflicting. We apply for credit cards without realizing that we'll be drowning in debt. We shop, we spend, we indulge ... and then we get heartbroken and stunt when it's time to pay bills. We simplify our beautiful languages to a minimum with jargons and slang to make things shorter and more convenient, when in reality, it sounds stupid and unorganized. We replace feelings and emotions with smileys and emojis.

Drowning ...

We are becoming impersonal, disconnected. We effortlessly use machines to do everything for us, counting on the technology for help in ... well, just about everything. We watch cartoons where characters don't speak but only use sounds, squeaks and screams. We watch movies with great sound effects and meaningless plots.

Disconnecting ...

We stopped searching for reasons in our actions, but rather act on impulses. We are all under the influence. We are under the influence of oversimplicity. How sad ... We worship stars on TV for their arrogance but find it useless and stupid even to watch real stars on a deep dark sky. What is happening to us? We degraded to listening to the modern music based on two similar beats but use classical music for plants and cows to increase harvest and milk production. How did primitive become new cool?

Another paradox—our kids. Why do we have kids? Well, so we have someone to blame for our anger issues, so quickly gone youth, sleepless nights and inability to finish a hundred things we start and abandon.

Searching ...

She's terrified to watch her beautiful world losing its mind. She is losing faith in her ridiculously crazy world, but she also believes..., believes in magic of life, magic of love, magic of music. While watching mysterious dark sky and listening to Symphony No. 41, she realizes how incredible it is to be a part of that magic. She understands the importance of loving kids to pieces for no particular reason, just because. She loves her World, the World that's losing its mind.

... Seems like we all just fell asleep... ★

CHAPTER NINETEEN
She is naked...

Be yourself, everyone else is already taken. So be you, be honest, be true. We are afraid to be honest, even when it comes to ourselves. We tell little white lies to make each other feel just a little better, finding it challenging to speak what's really on our minds. We hide from the past, and we are terrified of the future.

"Just kidding "reveals the truth behind the joke itself, something that is so incredibly important to us, that we want to stuff it deep into the joke, hoping no one would notice it. We all possess this power, power of hidden motives, hidden truths and hidden feelings. "I don't know" suppresses the hunger to share the knowledge, knowledge that you have but afraid no one cares to hear of, knowledge we bottle inside based on the ignorance of people around. People, who once made you feel invisible, what you think—unimportant and what you know—insignificant. And you just don't know, it is safer that way, right? We "don't care" anymore, even though our hearts are overwhelmed with emotions and feelings towards one another. Regardless of good or bad, positive or negative, black or white, it is easier to just not care. "I'm ok" carries a ton of pain, but we are too blind to notice, to care. We do not know what each one of us is going through, and quite honestly, we are too busy to care. We all are just ok.

We are so afraid to get "naked!" We are so afraid to show the world who we are, just the way we are.

She tries ... She tries so hard to be true, to stay true and give true ... true feelings, true emotions, true her. She is naked. She's not kidding, she knows, she cares, and she is not ok. She is not ok with this hidden world, beautiful but hidden world underneath ignorant and inconsiderate shell of indifference.

Say it ...

Listen to it ...

Say it, even if it's uncomfortable, when it's hard, at the risk of humiliating yourself. Say it, whisper it, scream it, write it, paint it, but don't hold it in. You're only hurting yourself. Find that one, pull them close and tell them how you feel.

Get naked ...

Be real ...

Stay true ...

... Afterall, every saint has a past and every sinner has a future. ★

CHAPTER TWENTY
She is slowing down…

Oh, how much stays unfinished, undone, untouched, unanswered, unsaid, things we are unaware of. It is unnecessary to have that many "uns" in our lives.

Telephone used to be a key … key to shortening the distance between us, key to connecting. She has a phone. Phone is no longer the key; it is the lock … big bulky stupid lock. It locks her in, it holds her captive. No ring … no text … it drives her crazy. How can you not go insane watching it minute by minute, and get nothing in return?

It's raining, it's gloomy and cold. She watches the rain drops hit the ground, glass … her. It's raining and it's cold. Phone is quiet, no ring, only rain drops, only white noise. Time goes by. It is incredible how much goes through her head, scenarios, feelings, emotions, all and nothing at the same time.

Say …

Do …

Touch …

Answer …

Finish …

By trying to be like others, we become no ones, we become invisible, we become weak. … Wait … There are no weak people in this world. Every one of us is a strong individual. We have powers, abilities to feel, to love, to believe, to hope, to dream and to live. We live by walking … walking our own paths, running our own marathons, driving through our own detours. We need to stop wasting our emotions on empty waiting, waiting for a phone to ring.

We gain, we lose … We lose a lot more than we gain. Why? Because we learn. We learn the value of thing, value of friends, value of pain and value of gain. We gain value, we lose useless stuff. Stuff we can live without. Lose it all, it only makes sense. Nature of a human being is to be hungry for enrichment, fulfilment and growth. Slow down! Chances are—you'll start noticing amazing things, bright opportunities, you will start growing and glowing.

Lose …

Wipe it all away …

Empty …

Let your life to deep clean your soul, your heart. Trust yourself, love yourself, be … yourself. Draw your own limits, break the barriers… They are not real.

Let go. Stop waiting. Phone does not ring. Value small things, be better, treasure every moment. And just like that, she is tired of waiting, waiting for the phone to wake up and make a sound. A sound she's been waiting and hoping for. Wasted time, countless rain drops, empty fall … She slows down, she finally notices that label on her favorite drink has a heart in the design, that her favorite song lyrics tell her to stay strong, that today is Wednesday, and … that it's no longer raining. No more waiting…

… She picks up the phone and dials the number. ★

FINAL CHAPTER
She is...

… me … she is you … she can be any one of us …

Maybe, just maybe… we all overvalue things that are essentially worthless…

We live at a very interesting time, time that doesn't slow down, time that doesn't wait, time that makes no sense and full of surprises at the same time.

Time …

Love …

You cannot make another person love you. All you can do is be you, be genuine, be Love. Be open to love, because the rest is just out of your reach. We spend years on earning each other's trust, but destroy it within seconds with the wrong word or look, if we are not careful. We are fragile, no matter how tough we want to seem to others. It is important to not just look good, but be good, be true. We need to know the difference between different "important" levels. What you have versus how you use what you have.

Realizing simple things …

I realize that in a blink of an eye, we can make someone happy or break their heart, affect someone for the rest of their life. I realize that forgiveness doesn't come easy to some, wisdom doesn't come because of the number of years you've walked on this Earth, but it does come base on what we've been through.

Anger drives us to things we can't take back. We have the right to be upset, which doesn't give us the right to be rude. Just like it is wrong to promise a child that everything they dream of is possible. It simply is not true. Kids have a tendency to believe us, trust us and love us unconditionally. Horror of horrors, what if they actually take what we say as the truth and later on realize the truth? A tragedy, broken dreams and impossibility of promises. Stop, we are killing magic … So, don't promise them everything they dream about, teach them to set up goals instead of empty dreams, but leave some magic there too. Some dreams have to stay dreams. Afterall, our kids are all we have left close to magic, they are magic.

Magic …

Time …

Magical time …

As humans, we are helpless, completely helpless. We hurt … we hurt each other and we hurt ourselves. And you know what happens when we're hurting? Nothing … The world does not stop, life keeps happening, clocks keep running forward. Time does not stop, it does not freeze, it does not pause.

Criticizing …

Forgiving …

I realize that we are our own worst critics and more often than not, we need to be able to forgive … ourselves rather than wait for forgiveness from others. The fact that we fight, does not prove we are miserable. The fact that we laugh, does not prove that we are happy. We don't always need to be learning and exposing each other secrets. Be careful, respectful and kind. Leave some of the things about yourself and your neighbor unknown, mystical, magical.

Weird enough, but the strangers may momentarily shift your life in an unpredictable direction. We don't always value one another, and that's why we lose … we lose one another. Just because people come and go, is not a good reason to keep discarding friend after friend. We can keep walking forward much longer after we've technically given up. We are tricky. Trust people, do not lose faith in us. Chances are—people helping you are the ones you least expect it from. Hardest time are the best scenarios to fall back on. Two different people produce two different paintings while following the same instructions. We are not at all the same. We all are unique and tricky. We need to be able to tell people we care about that they are our World, even though to the rest of the world it may mean nothing. Remember, question mark always makes it mysterious. The possibilities are endless.

SHE...

Possibilities …

True, everything is true, and everything is nonsense. We are lost … We are lost in the world of wrong priorities. Our kids walk around with amazing and cool iPhones based on the latest technology, when in reality, businesspeople would benefit from those. The importance of downloading a game on a gadget is set a priority over a scrabble or a crossword. What about our amazing kids, who are not by any means obligated to go to school, who gets to pick and choose when to continue their education? Maybe work a little first? When do kids stop being kids and fall into the world of responsibility, making money, building families and having fancy phones? Did we skip a step? … Or two?

We text each other while sitting in the same room, just to avoid eye contact, forgetting that looking at each other was once romantic and nerve-racking. We try to make each other jealous. Weddings cost thousands of dollars and tons of stress. We overcompensate our extravagant automobiles with low-income houses. This "I wanna be cool" syndrome becomes contagious. The necessity to appear better than others becomes priority number one. An amazing weekend spent at home is laughed at, just the same as a kid without a phone at school.

What happened to us? We are in real danger. We don't invest in what's important, we invest in attention. We get in debt while trying to promote who we really aren't, we worry about other people and their perception of us. Poor us, poor humans. We are so confused.

do yourself a favor…

… promise yourself to be you…

In reality, we are all looking for something, constantly, repeatedly, blindly. Maybe we even get blind in the process. We constantly walk into the world if uncertainty called "future." Some walk with us, by our side, some get left behind, in the past. The important thing is—to not get lost, don't lose yourself behind, and don't look back. Don't ever look back! Don't regret leaving people behind, don't regret leaving things behind, don't regret … Just do not regret! Get away from this pointless and annoying feeling of regret. Leave it, leave it all in the past, and keep walking forward. It is all a part of our extraordinary adventures.

Our lives are so beautifully complicated and complex. We all want to feel secure, loved and cared for, that we start complicating things. We are convinced that by complicating things, we protect ourselves, our loved ones, our hearts. And then it all begins … the more complicating our lives become, the more insecure we feel about ourselves. That is what's wrong with us, we are tricky, we are incredibly smart and dumb all at once. We are all very conflicting, we all are. We are all searching … and in the attempt to discover our true selves, we burry ourselves in, deeper and deeper.

Searching …

Regretting …

Complicating …

Failing …

We buy each other things we'll never need, but fail to share the most important thing of all—love and time spent together. We need to wake up, we need to stop caring about others, other people's opinions and values! Remember you! Let go of everything, learn to let go. People will always find reasons to be jealous of you. Yes, you! Jealousy will come without labels, cool cars and money. There always will be something, and that something will eat others whole, no matter what. Jealous people are everywhere. So why don't we try instead of seeming to be in control, we can actually be in control. Believe in you, remember you! The unique you. Stop asking and hoping for everyone's approval to be … you.

Don't look down at people after you've become better, but look up … look up at people you value, appreciate and love. Genuine love is a rarity. Only then you truly become a happy individual, and that would be the best label you'll ever wear. Believe in magic, believe in … You … Become a treasure. ★